YOUR FAVOURITE
ANIMALS of FARTHING WOOD
STORY COLLECTION

DEAN

Contents

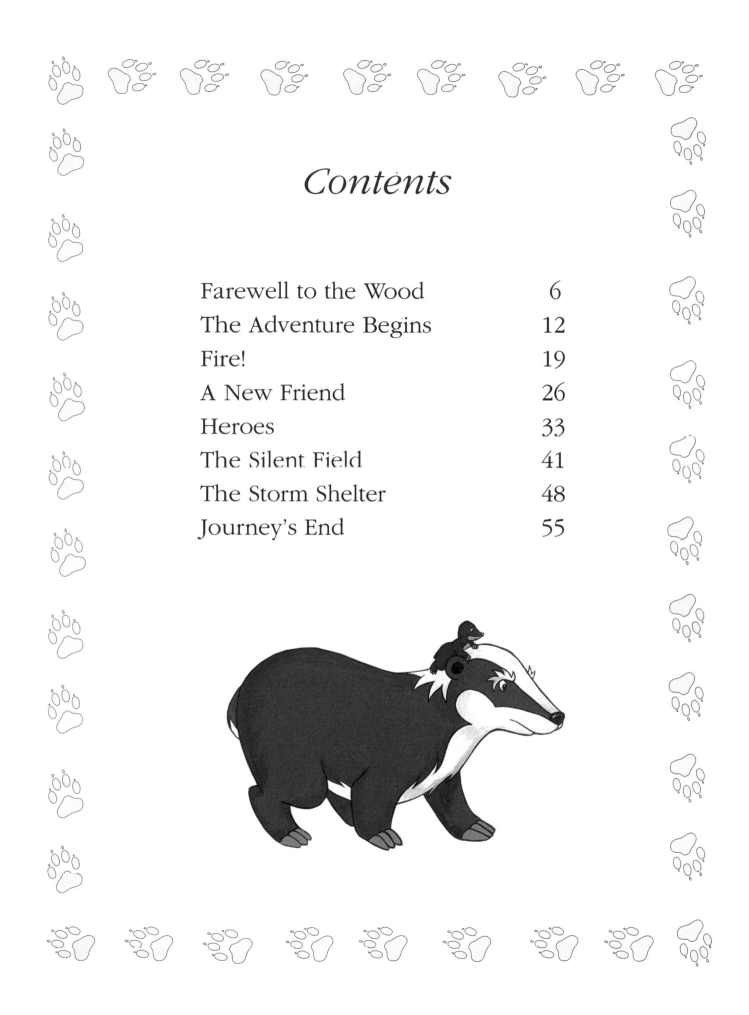

Farewell To The Wood

Toad was hot. Toad was tired. But Toad was happy. At last he was coming home to Farthing Wood.

He hopped slowly, dragging his tired legs on the rough ground. "If I can just keep going a little longer —" he panted. "I'll soon be home."

Suddenly, a shadow fell across him. Toad heard a grinding noise of gears shifting, then a giant metal claw scooped him up!

Toad shouted frantically. "Help! Put me down!" The claw turned over, and tipped Toad out. A pile of earth and stones fell on top of him.

In another part of Farthing Wood, Badger, Weasel and Owl were worried.

"It's terrible," said Badger, shaking his head. "They're cutting down more of the wood every day."

"Ha! They would, wouldn't they?" said Weasel. "They're human, after all."

"How many homes have gone today, Owl?" asked Badger.

Owl ticked them off on her claws. "Half a dozen burrows, three squirrel dreys and fifteen birds' nests," she said. In the distance, another tree crashed to the ground. "That makes sixteen," said Owl.

Kestrel swooped down to perch beside Owl. "Have you heard?" she said. "They're filling in the pond!"

Owl gasped. Badger groaned. Weasel tried

6

to look cheerful.

"At least we've still got the stream," she pointed out.

"But it's only a muddy trickle now," said

Badger gloomily. "Come and see."

Some hedgehogs and rabbits were trying to drink at the few remaining puddles.

Suddenly, they squeaked with fright. Fox had arrived.

"This is a crisis," he said. "Make no mistake. We can't live without water."

"What can we do?" said everyone together.

Fox thought for a moment. "We must call an Assembly," he said at last.

"But they're only supposed to be for emergencies," said Badger.

"What do you call this, then?" said Weasel cheekily. "A picnic?"

"What g-good will an Assembly do?" squeaked a brave little rabbit.

"I don't know," said Fox, "but we've got to do something."

"He's right," said Badger, as Fox slipped away. "We'll meet at midnight in my set. Rabbit, you tell Hare. Hedgehog, you find the newts. Weasel can look for the voles."

"What about Mole?" said Weasel.

"Moley will find his way," said Badger.

Everyone scurried away to spread the news.

"An Assembly! At midnight!" called the squirrels in the treetops.

"In Badger's set!" squeaked the shrews in the long grass.

"We've forgotten our snakey friend, Adder," said Weasel with a shudder.

"Find her then," said Badger, "but warn her to behave."

As night fell, Badger got to work. Clods of earth flew out of his set.

"Watch out!" said Weasel, passing by. Badger came up blinking.

"Sorry," he said. "I'm trying to make more room down here. Why don't you fetch some glow worms? We're going to need their light."

Midnight came. Owl arrived first. She snapped her beak crossly.

"You don't expect me to go down there?" she said. "Why, I might get dirty!"

"Old fuss-pot," said Weasel rudely.

"Please, Owl," said Badger hastily. "I need you to set an example."

"Oh, in that case..." said Owl, and down the set she went.

Everyone else followed.

"Not lassst, am I?" said Adder, at the end of the line.

"Yes, you are," said Badger, "and Adder, don't eat the glow worms!"

"Of courssse I won't!" said Adder, but she did look disappointed.

When all of the animals had settled down, Badger cleared his throat.

"Now listen, everyone," he began.

"Wait," said Weasel. "Where's Mole?"

There was a sudden scrabbling noise overhead, and a crack appeared in the roof of the set, then one paw, and then another.

"Sorry I'm late, everyone," said Mole in a small voice.

Fox stepped forward. "Animals," he said, "we're in great danger. Our wood is being destroyed and our pond has gone. Once it was home to forty-seven toads. The last one left months ago, and never returned..."

Outside, in the darkness of Farthing Wood, something was moving. Toad, bruised and dazed, had managed at last to dig his way out of the pile of earth on top of him.

"I'm still alive!" he croaked. "And I'm home! At least, I think I am. But where is everyone?"

Toad looked round. In the moonlight he saw Farthing Wood. It looked smaller than he remembered.

"I'm coming, mateys," he called, painfully hopping along. "Toad's here! Toad's back! I'm coming!"

Suddenly, he felt the soft earth give way beneath him. He was falling again, down and down into the ground!

He nearly landed right on Weasel's tail.

"Well, bless my soul, it's that daft Toad," sniffed Owl. "I thought you were gone for good."

"So did I," said Toad, smiling round at all his friends.

"Where have you been all this time, Toad?" asked Rabbit.

"Where haven't I been, more like," said Toad. "Caught in a jam jar, I was, and carried far away by a nasty human child. But I bided my time, and escaped. I've been travelling for months. Horrible, it was. 'I  must get back to my mateys,' I kept thinking. 'I must get back to my pond.'"

There was an awkward silence.

9

"The pond isss gone," said Adder. "Filled in."

"What?" gasped Toad. "No! It isn't true!"

being destroyed. We've got to leave. That's why we've called an Assembly."

He turned to the birds. "Can you help us? You travel far and wide. Is there another

pond nearby?"

Pheasant shook his head. "My wife and I never venture out of the wood," he said. "We might be, er—"

Tears trickled out of his large, staring eyes.

"I'm sorry, Toad," said Fox, "but you might as well know the truth. Farthing Wood is

"Shot," said Hen Pheasant bluntly.

"I know a place where we could go," said Toad quietly. "It's a perfect place. No humans anywhere. Only animals allowed."

"Only animals?" everyone echoed in

disbelief. "Where? Tell us where!"

"It's called White Deer Park," said Toad. "It's a nature reserve. It's a terribly long journey, but I could lead you there."

Fox looked at Badger. Badger nodded.

"We have no choice," said Fox. "White Deer Park it must be. But first..." He looked round at the ring of faces.

"We must take the Ancient Woodland Vow. We must all promise to help one another and..." Now he looked particularly at Adder, Weasel and Owl. "... *not* to eat each other."

Everyone started talking at once.

"We must have a leader," said Badger. "Someone brave, and cunning, and strong."

"Fox! Fox!" the animals shouted.

"Thank you," said Fox. "Here's my first order. Rest and eat for one more day. We'll start our journey tomorrow at midnight."

The animals agreed and said goodnight.

Badger gazed around his set.

"My home sweet home," he whispered sadly. "Farewell, Farthing Wood."

The Adventure Begins

Farthing Wood was being destroyed. Humans had chopped down many of the trees, and filled in the pond. The animals were in great danger.

"Follow me," Fox said to them. "I'll lead you to White Deer Park, a place of safety for us all. It will be a terrible journey, but Toad will show us the way."

Badger looked round at the group of anxious little animals. "Rabbits, hedgehogs, mice, voles, squirrels," he said, counting them off on his claws. "Weasel, Adder, Hare, Owl, Kestrel — "

Quickly Mole hid before Badger could call his name. He was afraid to leave the wood.

"Oh dear," said Badger. "Where's Mole?"

It was midnight and the great adventure was about to begin.

Badger was sad. His family had lived in Farthing Wood for hundreds of years.

But the squirrels were happy. "Yippee! An adventure!" they squeaked.

Poor Mole was worried. "I'm too slow to keep up," he thought.

"Are we all here, Badger?" asked Fox.

"We've a long way to go before dawn, Badger," said Fox quietly. "We can't wait."

"But we can't leave Mole behind," Badger protested. "I'll stay and look for him. We'll catch you up."

"Right," said Fox.

12

"Now let's go."

The time had come. The little group of animals left their homes in the wood, and set off into the night.

Badger looked round the woodland clearing.

"Mole!" he shouted. "Where's he got to? Silly Moley. Hiding as usual!"

There was no answer. Nothing stirred in Farthing Wood. Then suddenly, a little mound of earth appeared at Badger's feet.

"Mole!" said Badger sternly. "I know you're down there. Come out at once!"

"I'm not coming out," said Mole in a small voice. Badger had to lean over to hear him. "I'm not coming with you. You can beg and plead all you like. I'm staying here."

"But why?" asked Badger.

"Because I'm s-stupid, and s-slow. I can't go as fast as everyone else. I'll hold you up."

"Don't be silly, Mole, old chap," growled Badger. "I'll look after you."

"You will?" gulped Mole.

"Of course," promised Badger.

Mole shot out of the ground. He was smiling now. Gently, Badger picked him up and put him on his back. Then he trotted off after the others.

The animals had been travelling for hours.

"We must find water soon," said the newts, "or our baby will die."

Owl flew off to look for water. Soon she was back. "Follow me," she hooted.

"There's a swimming pool near here. Not far now!"

The little animals struggled over the rough ground, gasping for breath, while Owl led the way. They followed her past a fence and into a garden.

"Water," croaked the newts feebly.

"Quick, over here!" called Owl.

Everyone rushed forward to the pool.

"Don't make a noise," warned Fox. "There are humans about!"

At last the newts reached the pool and dived straight in. They drank and splashed and swam, twisting and turning in the cool water. Their baby was better at once.

Toad bounded in after them. "Come on, mateys!" he called to all the other animals. "Come on in for a swim!"

Everyone crowded round the pool.

"Cor, that's better," slurped Weasel.

"Remarkably enjoyable," spluttered Owl.

"It's not fair! We can't reach the water," the little ones squeaked.

Fox and Badger lay down with their snouts nearly touching the water.

"Run down our backs," said Fox. "You'll be able to drink then."

Toad was having a wonderful time.

"Oo! Whee! Yippee!" he sang happily, as he hopped in and out of the pool. He nearly tipped the rabbits in.

"Don't get us wet!" they squealed.

A light went on in the house.

"Silly Toad!" called Fox. "Now you've woken the humans. Get out of the water, everyone! Hurry!"

The animals scrambled clear of the pool.

"Follow Owl," barked Fox. "Badger, help everyone through the fence!"

In the house, more lights went on. Suddenly, the cat flap in the back door swung open, and a cat appeared.

"Grr," he said as the tasty mice filed past. The cat licked his lips and pushed, trying to force his fat body through the cat flap.

"Fox!" called Badger. "Come quickly!"

Fox hurried to the cat flap, followed closely by Adder.

"What's this?" the cat said when he saw Adder slithering outside his door.

"I feel bad, riding on you when the others are so tired," said Mole.

Kestrel flew up to Fox. "Kee! Kee!" she called. "Dawn is coming soon, Fox. I'll find a place for us to rest during the day."

Kestrel soon flew back. "There's a big gorse thicket nearby," she told Fox, "but it's on army land, and — " she hesitated.

"Yes?" said Fox.

"We'll have to cross a road to get there," Kestrel answered.

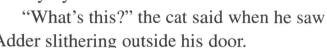

Fox saw his chance while the cat was distracted. Quickly, he slammed the cat flap shut and the cat disappeared.

On and on the animals went. Their tails drooped and their feet dragged in the dust.

Badger heard Mole give a big sigh. "What's the matter, Moley?" he asked.

The animals lined up at the edge of the road. Kestrel hovered overhead.

"Go now while there are no cars!" she called. "Quick!"

Badger led the first group. The baby rabbits kept trying to break away.

"Don't panic!" their mother scolded. "Follow Badger!"

Toad was the last to cross. He hopped into the road. It seemed miles and miles to the other side.

"Come on, Toad! You can do it! Hurry, or you'll get squashed!" his friends shouted.

But Toad was very tired.

"I'm coming, mateys," he croaked feebly. "Toady's coming!"

"Go! Go!" shouted Fox from the roadside.

Adder led the second group. She looked hungrily at the mice and voles. "Come with me, my dearsss," she hissed.

"Adder, stop teasing," said Fox sternly.

Suddenly, a huge lorry came roaring down the road towards Toad.

"Oh no!" gasped Toad. "I'm a gonner!"

He rolled over onto his back, and lay still, waiting for the lorry to run him over. To the amazement of the animals, the lorry stopped just in time. The driver got out and bent down to look at Toad.

"What have we got here?" he said

There was a furious beating of wings in the air. The man looked up as Owl's sharp beak and strong talons scratched at his head.

"Oi! Get off! Stop that!" he said.

"Now's your chance! Run for it, Toad!" the animals shouted.

Toad opened his eyes and sat up.

"I'm not dead!" he said. "Wee hee!"

"I'm coming to get you, Toad," called Fox.

Owl struck at the man again and he climbed back into his cab, cursing.

Quick as a flash, Fox ran up to Toad. "Catch hold of my tail! Quick!"

Toad grabbed Fox's tail, and held on tight until they had safely reached the other side of the road.

"You saved my life, matey!" gasped Toad, dropping off Fox's tail.

17

"And so did Owl," said Fox.

Owl blinked and looked pleased. "It's nice to be appreciated," she said.

It was only a few steps more to the peace and safety of the gorse thicket. Everyone lay down at once.

Gently, Badger set Mole down on the ground. Mole sighed wearily.

"My dear companions," Badger began. "I'd like to say, to one and all, how proud I am to be a member of this valiant

company." Badger paused. "Eh? Did somebody say something?"

"Zzzz," snored the other animals. Badger smiled.

"Goodnight, my friends," he said, and a minute later, he was fast asleep too."

The animals of Farthing Wood had been travelling all night. Now at last they slept.

Badger dreamed of his old set. Tomorrow, giant digger machines would destroy it.

Owl dreamed of her favourite perch. The big oak tree had

been sawn down already to make room for new houses.

Fox slept lightly. As leader of the animals, he had to be watchful, day and night.

"Follow me, mateys," croaked Toad in his sleep. "I'm the only one who knows the way

to the nature reserve. It's safe there."

And what about Mole? He was dreaming of fat, juicy worms, as usual.

Suddenly, there was a huge explosion.

"A-an earthquake!" cried Mother Rabbit.

"Don't panic!" squealed Father Rabbit. "Oh, my poor nerves!"

"It seems the shooting season's started early," said Fox. "How very unsporting."

Kestrel flew off to see what was happening.

"Kee! Kee!" she called, coming in to land. "There are soldiers! This is army land."

"It's time to travel on," said Fox.

"But where's Mole?" said Badger.

A little snout pushed up through the earth, and the rest of Mole followed it.

"Sorry," he said, gulping down a worm. "Just finishing my breakfast."

Kestrel led them down to the marsh.

They flopped into the cool marsh with a sigh of relief. Toad followed right behind. Fox looked at them anxiously.

"You're tired out already," he said.

"Don't worry about me," croaked Toad bravely. "I like long walks. But the newts can't go on. Why don't they stay here?"

"Yes!" said the newts. "We'll stay here."

"All right," said Fox. "Good luck, newts."

"Hooray!" squeaked Baby Newt. "We're going to live in the marsh!" He splashed the water with his tail.

Fox rounded up the other animals.

"We must get round the marsh before nightfall," he said. "It's time to go."

"Must we?" said Mole. "The worms here are the biggest, nicest, juiciest..."

"One day, Mole," said Owl severely, "you'll be so fat you'll get stuck in one of your own tunnels."

They set off. Adder was behind the mice.

"I sssimply adore a fat moussse," she teased.

The mice scattered in terror.

"Adder!" barked Fox. "Stop that!"

No one saw the car that passed along the

road behind them, or the careless human tossing a cigarette end into the dry grass.

Weasel was the first to smell the smoke.

"Fire!" she squealed. "And I'm not joking

this time! Honest!"

The rabbits had been fooled before.

"You're teasing, as usual," they said.

"Since we've stopped anyway..." muttered Mole, sliding off Badger's back. A minute later, he was digging for worms.

"Where's Toad?" asked Fox. "We mustn't lose our guide. Where..."

Suddenly, Kestrel swooped down. "Fire! Fire!" she mewed. "Danger! Run!"

The rabbits quivered in terror.

"Don't panic! Don't panic!" shrieked Mother Rabbit, bolting the wrong way.

"Come back!" shouted Badger gruffly. "We must stick together!"

Fox could see the fire now. He could feel the heat of the flames, and hear their terrifying crackle. Clouds of billowing smoke made him cough and splutter.

His instinct told him to run, but he stood his ground.

"I must save the others," he thought.

"And I must find Toad! He's our guide!"

"Kestrel!" he called. "Lead everyone to the other side of the marsh! The big ones must go slowly, and wait for the smallest."

"We can't go yet," said Badger anxiously. "We've lost Mole! And Adder!"

Adder slithered out of the smoke. "How sssweet of you to wait," she said.

"Oh Moley, where are you?" said Badger.

"Come now!" called Kestrel. "Follow me! Kee! Kee!"

Fox was shaking with fear, but he ran back towards the fire.

"Where are you going, Fox?" said Kestrel.

"I must find Toad!" replied Fox.

The smoke was choking him. The flames were blinding him. But he ran on and on.

"Toad!" he called. "Where are you?"

Toad croaked feebly. He was crouching near the ground, waiting to die.

"I'm coming, Toad!" coughed Fox.

Toad looked up. "You came back for me," he gasped. "Thanks, matey."

Fox picked Toad up gently in his mouth, and ran out of the fire to safety.

While the fire raged overhead, Mole was busy digging underground. He heard

Badger's voice calling to him, but just then a juicy worm caught his eye.

"A few more minutes won't hurt," he said greedily, and started gobbling up the worm. Finally, he dug his way up to the surface.

Mole made a little mound of earth as he dug himself out of the ground. When he popped to the surface, he

looking for a way out. "Fox," she called. "There's an island, with a causeway running out to it. You can cross there. The water's shallow. But be quick! The fire is getting closer!"

It was easy for the big animals to cross the causeway, but the little ones stood on the bank, chattering with fear.

"We can't cross on our own! We'll drown!" they squeaked.

"Climb aboard, then," said Badger.

The smaller animals climbed onto Badger and Fox and held on tightly as they crossed to the safety of the island.

found the fire brigade dousing the flames with their long hoses. The ground was charred and soaked.

A fireman saw him. "Poor little chap," he said, and he picked Mole up and put him in his pocket.

The fire was quickly spreading to the other side of the marsh where the animals bunched together anxiously.

Kestrel hovered,

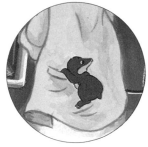

Mole peeped out of the fireman's pocket. The jacket was slung over the door of the fire engine. Quickly, Mole scrambled out of the pocket.

"Look, there's Mole!" called Kestrel.

"Moley will never find us here," said Fox. "Owl, if you and Kestrel distract the firefighters, I'll go and fetch him."

23

"Where are Badger and the others?" Mole wondered as he climbed to the ground.

Just then, there was a "Whoo-hoo!" from Owl, and a "Kee! Kee!" from Kestrel, and the two birds soared into the air. They dived and turned above the firefighters' heads in a dazzling flying display.

The firefighters watched in amazement.

Fox saw his chance. He darted across the causeway and ran up to Mole, who was peering blindly round with his short-sighted eyes, not knowing which way to run.

"Quick! Climb up my tail!" said Fox.

"Wh-what? Wh-where?" said Mole. Then he saw Fox's brush, and jumped onto it.

One of the firefighters saw them.

"Cor! Look at that fox!" he said, and all the firefighters turned round.

"And there are more animals on that island!" said another. "Rabbits, hedgehogs, squirrels and a badger, all together. Poor little creatures. Let's leave them in peace."

The animals watched the firefighters go.

"Oh, thank you, Fox! Thank you!" sobbed Mole. "I've been so silly! I promise I'll never be greedy again. I thought I'd lost you forever, and I missed you so much,

especially you, Badger."

Badger picked up his little friend. "And I missed you, Moley," he said.

A drop of rain fell on Toad's head.

"Ah-ha! Rain!" he chuckled happily.

"Not everyone likes rain," the rabbits sniffed. "We need to be warm and dry."

"Follow me, everyone," said Fox. "Let's go and look for shelter so we can have a rest."

"Good thinking, Fox!" said Badger, and all of the other animals agreed.

Fox and Vixen were catching rats.

"This is good," said Fox. "It's been weeks since I hunted. I wish I could stay here with you, but I must go and find my friends again."

He told Vixen about the animals of Farthing Wood, their long journey to the nature reserve, and how he had lost them.

"Don't you eat the mice and rabbits?" asked Vixen, amazed.

"They're my friends," said Fox. "We travel together. I couldn't hunt them."

Vixen shivered. "People hunt foxes around here, with horses, and hounds, and whips, too."

"We'll have to be careful," said Fox.

Not far away, a group of very tired animals were following a huffing, puffing Toad up a steep hill.

"Nearly there, mateys!" croaked Toad.

"Let me get down, Badger," said Mole. "You're so tired. I can walk the last bit."

"Nonsense, Moley," rumbled Badger. "You're no trouble. Half the time, I don't even know you're there."

But he was talking to himself. Mole had already slipped off his back, and was struggling feebly up the hill.

Adder slithered past him. "Lossst your transsssport?" she hissed.

Weasel jumped over him. "Ha! Ha! Moley's lost!" she jeered.

"Oh dear! Badger, help!" called Mole.

Fox had picked up the scent of his friends.

"They're near here!" he called to Vixen. He ran back to her. "Will you come with me?" he asked. "I'd like you

to be my mate, then we could always be together."

Vixen hesitated. "Perhaps," she said. "I'll decide as we go along."

"Let's go then," said Fox as he followed the scent. He was full of hope.

But further on, the scent divided.

"They must have doubled back," said Fox. "I hope they haven't got lost."

"You follow one trail, and I'll follow the other," Vixen suggested, and she raced off.

"You will come back, won't you?" Fox called after her.

Vixen didn't reply.

The trail took her into the wood, where she noticed a thrush feeding her babies.

"Don't you miss your freedom?" asked Vixen thoughtfully.

"I haven't time," said Thrush, stuffing another worm into a hungry little beak.

"I don't know what to do," sighed Vixen.

"Met a male fox, have you?" said Thrush. "Is he brave? And true?"

"Probably," said Vixen.

They both laughed.

"If you don't try, you'll never know," Thrush told her.

"Thank you, Thrush," said Vixen.

Suddenly, the sound of a horn echoed through the wood.

"The hunt!" Vixen whispered, her body trembling in terror.

"Run! Run for your life!" shrilled Thrush.

Mole reached the top at last.

"Moley, there you are!" said Badger. "I was worried. Why did you get off me?"

"Oh, Badger," sobbed Mole. "You were so tired, and I wanted to help, and oh dear, I've been a nuisance again."

"Kee! Kee! The hunters have picked up a scent," said Kestrel.

The hounds bounded into the wood. Their noses twitched at the scent of the foxes. They panted with excitement.

Poor Mole was still battling up the hill.

"Help! Badger!" he bleated feebly.

The ground shook beneath him, and a frightful thundering noise made him jump.

"Oh dear! An earthquake!" yelped Mole.

Kestrel saw him, and hovered overhead.

"Keep going, Mole! You're nearly there," she called.

Then they stopped, confused. There were two trails. There must be two foxes!

The Master galloped up. "That way!" he ordered, pointing with his whip.

The hounds set off on Vixen's trail.

Vixen ran faster than she had ever run before. Her breath came in heaving gasps and her legs felt heavy. She was exhausted.

Fox raced back up the hill. He was tiring.

"If I can only - reach - the wood at the top of the hill!" he panted.

He could hear the hounds behind him. They were gaining quickly!

"I'm done for," thought Fox. "Oh Vixen, Vixen, I hope you're safe!"

"There's no way out! They'll get me!" she thought desperately.

Fox had run from the hunt, too. He started to race up the hill, but when he looked back he could see Vixen breaking out of the trees.

The hounds were closing in!

"I must save her! I must save Vixen!" he thought, and he ran back down the hill straight towards the hounds.

The animals on the hilltop saw him go.

"It's Fox! Our Fox!" gasped Badger.

"What's happening?" piped up Mole.

"Kee! Kee! He's trying to head off the hounds to save the vixen!" said Kestrel.

"But some of the hounds are still after her!"

"Oh, my poor nerves," squealed Father Rabbit, and he fainted.

The animals watched in terror.

"He's leading the hunt to us!" howled Weasel, and she jumped into a bush.

"He hasn't seen us yet," said Badger. "Stand firm, all of you. Get ready to fight!"

"But we'll be torn to pieces," shrieked Weasel, from inside her bush.

"Owl! Kestrel! Do your best," said Badger.

The birds flew out of the wood, swooping and diving on the Master and his hounds.

"I say, get the hounds back," called the Master. "Let's go for the other fox."

The hunt retreated down the hill, and Fox crawled, exhausted, into the wood.

"Fox! It really is you!" said his friends, crowding round him.

"Kee! Kee! Don't worry, you're safe," said Kestrel. "They've gone after the vixen."

"I've failed her, then," groaned Fox.

"What do you mean?" said Badger gently.

"I wanted her to be my mate," wept Fox.

"Bet she gets away," cackled Weasel. "Three to one odds. Any takers?"

"Weasel," growled Badger. "Shut up!"

Vixen was out of the wood now, and using the last of her  strength to run up the hill. Her flanks heaved and her tail drooped.

Then she fell. In a flash, the Master's horse was on her. He lifted his whip, ready to strike Vixen's head.

The horse shied, whinnying in pain. The Master lost his seat and fell heavily. He lay still on the ground. The hounds milled around in confusion. The other huntsmen ran up.

"Call off the hunt," one said. "The Master's hurt."

The horn sounded again. The hunt turned away, the Master limping along behind it.

Silently, Vixen slipped into the wood.

"What's going on?" asked Father Rabbit, waking up from his faint.

"Fox and the vixen are

safe," said Badger with a sigh of relief. "The hunt is over."

"Why did they go?" asked Weasel.

"Kee! Kee!" said Kestrel. "I saw a snake strike at the horse's leg."

Fox could do nothing to save her. "I can't look," he said, hiding his face.

Then something small and slim and slithery slipped through the grass. It was Adder. She reared up, and sank her fangs into the horse's foreleg.

"Ha ha! Adder's a heroine!" sniggered Weasel. "Who'd have thought it? Ah ha ha ha!"

"It wasss sssome other ssstupid sssnake," said Adder, looking embarrassed.

"Don't believe you! Can't fool me!" chanted Weasel.

"Fox," said Vixen shyly. "You saved me!"

Fox nuzzled her. "Vixen, will you...?"

"Yes," said Vixen. "I'll be your mate."

Badger stepped forward. "Welcome, my dear," he said. "You're one of us, now."

Fox nuzzled Vixen again. "Now we can go to the nature reserve together, where we'll always be safe."

The animals of Farthing Wood had found their lost leader. Fox's new mate, Vixen, was

squeaked the mice and voles.

Kestrel, who had flown up high to spy out the land, swooped down again.

with him.

"Oh Fox, you're safe," sobbed Mole.

"Crying again, Moley!" said Badger. "What a shame your tears are salty. If they weren't, we'd never

have to go thirsty!"

"I'm thirsty now!" said Baby Rabbit.

"Me too!"

"Kee! Follow me!" she cried. "There's an old quarry nearby and it's full of water!"

"I remember it, mateys!" said Toad. "Lovely it is. A treat of a place!"

But a fence surrounded the quarry.

33

"What'sss all the fusss about?" said Adder. She slipped through the fence with ease, hissing at the mice and voles along the way.

Mole slid down off Badger's back.

"I could make a tunnel underneath, couldn't I, Badger?" he said.

"Oh, Moley!" said Badger, smiling at his friend. "What would we do without you?"

Mole started at once.

"You're digging in the wrong direction!" said Weasel, and screamed with laughter.

"Oh, sorry," said Mole.

Mole started digging again. Soil flew out of the hole and onto the other animals.

"Oi! Stop it!" shouted Father Rabbit.

"My husband's being buried alive!" cried

Mother Rabbit in a panic.

"He's all right," said Fox sternly.

Mole popped out of his new tunnel on the other side of the fence. The hedgehogs dived down after him.

"Wait!" said Mole. "Let Badger look at it first. It is a good tunnel, isn't it, Badger?"

"Very good indeed," said Badger. "Well done, Moley."

Mole glowed with pride.

Soon, everyone was drinking at the water's edge. Vixen looked round at her new friends. Weasel was teasing Adder. Owl was asleep. Mole and Toad were grubbing in the mud for worms.

"Look at greedy Mole!" she laughed.

"Toad's greedy too," said Mole, with his mouth full.

"So I am, mateys! So I am!" said Toad.

Suddenly, there was a strange whistling

noise overhead. The animals looked up, startled. A heron was flying over the water,

his great wings beating the air. He dived into the water, scooping up a fish.

The little animals scrambled for cover. Even Adder slipped quietly under a rock.

The heron landed.

"Good evening," he said politely.

"I hope you don't mind us being here in your quarry, Heron," said Fox.

"Guests are always welcome," said the heron. "And please, call me Whistler."

"Funny name," said Weasel rudely.

Whistler showed her his wing. "A human shot at me once," he said. "The bullet made a hole in my wing. Now the air whistles through it when I fly."

"The noise must make hunting difficult," said Owl.

"Fish can't hear," said Whistler. "Watch."

He took off, and plunged into the water. A second later he surfaced, carrying a gleaming fish in his beak.

Toad was watching excitedly. "I can fish too! Look at me, mateys!" he shouted, and dived into the water.

Owl looked on disapprovingly. "Pride goes before a fall," she said.

36

Toad didn't hear. He had seen a fish. He darted through the water after it.

"I'll show 'em," he thought happily.

He caught the fish by the tail, then surfaced. He didn't see the big carp hiding in the reeds, waiting for him.

"Look what I've got!" Toad shouted.

The carp was right underneath him now. She opened her gaping mouth, and pulled Toad back under the water.

The carp was hungry, but Toad was fat. Try as she might, she couldn't swallow him. She thrashed about in the water.

The animals watched anxiously from the bank.

"Where's Toad got to now?" asked Fox. "We mustn't lose him. He's our guide!"

"He's been caught!" said Whistler. "I'll

take care of that old carp."

He dived into the water, his sharp beak searching. The carp tried to swim away, but her heavy mouthful slowed her down. She was no match for the heron. Whistler snapped her up, Toad and all, and dropped them onto the bank. Toad fell out of the carp's mouth.

"Is Toad dead?" squeaked Baby Rabbit.

37

Whistler sighed, picked up the carp, and dropped her back in the water.

"You're a funny lot, you are," he said.

"We're fellow travellers," said Fox. "We've taken an oath to help and protect each other while we're on our journey."

"Stand aside, please," ordered Weasel. She picked Toad up by the feet and shook him.

"He's opened his eyes!" said Mole. Tears of joy splashed down his cheeks.

"Thank you, Whistler," croaked Toad in a shaky voice. "You're a hero."

The carp was gasping on the bank, dying slowly. Toad felt a pang of sympathy.

"Throw her back in, matey," he said to Whistler. "Poor thing. She's in agony."

"But she was going to eat you," said Whistler. "Anyway, I've been trying to catch her for years."

"Please," said Toad. "One more favour."

"*Live and let live*, that's our motto," Badger explained to the heron.

"How interesting," Whistler remarked.

"I suppose you want to come with us," cackled Weasel.

 "Well, actually..." said Whistler.

"You're welcome to join us," said Fox.

"But first you must take the Oath!" twittered the mice anxiously.

"Very well," said Whistler. "I promise not to eat any of you. Will that do?"

"Yesss! It will!" hissed Adder, relieved.

It was time to leave the quarry and travel on. Toad and Fox led the way.

"Nearly there, mateys!" Toad called out

encouragingly. "Not far now!"

"That sssilly whissstling noissse isss getting on my nervesss!" grumbled Adder, looking up at Whistler.

Suddenly, a shot rang out. Toad was so startled, he dropped off Fox's back.

Kestrel dived down from the sky. "Kee! Kee! There are hunters nearby. Take care!"

Fox barked out orders. "Keep together everyone! Get under the hedge. Quick! Rabbits, don't panic!"

Vixen was trembling at Fox's side. "Oh Fox," she whispered. "I hear dogs!"

"We'll have a better chance if we all keep still," Fox said grimly.

The rabbits' eyes were wide with fear and their noses twitched in alarm. "Don't panic! Don't panic!" Mother Rabbit whispered frantically.

The dogs were close now. Everyone froze.

Even Baby Rabbit was as quiet as he could be. Finally he could bear the tension no longer. Silly with fear, he darted into the clearing.

A moment later the animals heard a loud explosion. Baby Rabbit fell over.

"Oh, my baby!" shrieked Mother Rabbit.

She started to run to the clearing, but Badger held her back.

"It's no good," he said gently.

A man with a gun picked up the little rabbit and dropped him into his bag.

Sadly, the animals watched the hunter leave the wood with the bag slung over his shoulder.

"Baby Rabbit saved us," said Badger softly. "That hunter would have found us all if Baby Rabbit hadn't distracted him. He's a hero."

"Yes, he is," Fox agreed. "Unfortunately, the motto *Live and let live* doesn't mean anything to some humans."

He looked round at his little band of travellers. The mice, hares and squirrels had crowded round to comfort the poor rabbits. Overhead, the birds kept watch.

"Glad you joined us, Whistler?" Fox called to the heron.

"Oh yes!" Whistler replied. "I'm proud to have friends like you."

The Silent Field

The cabbage field was very still and quiet. The animals of Farthing Wood looked round uneasily.

"We're safe here, anyway," said Badger.

No one answered. They were just glad to have got this far on their journey. When bulldozers had invaded their home in Farthing Wood, the animals had set off on the dangerous trek to the nature reserve, where humans wouldn't bother them.

Tra la...."

Hare pounced on Weasel and clamped her mouth shut with his paws.

"Humph!" said Weasel indignantly. She shook Hare off. "What's wrong with a good old sing-song, I'd like to know?"

"It's too noisy, that's what's wrong," said

"Come on, mateys," croaked Toad. "Follow me. We're near White Deer Park now. It's lovely there. You mark my words...."

His voice died away. It was too quiet in this vast, silent field.

"Tra la la!" sang out Weasel suddenly, making everyone jump. "We need a marching song. Something to cheer us up.

Hare sternly. "I'm sure you could be heard from miles away."

Fox had moved on with Toad. He looked back at the group of animals behind him.

"Why have you stopped, Badger?" he called to his friend.

"There's something strange about this

field," Badger replied. "I'm worried."
"Well, I'm not worried," said Mole.
"I'm hungry."

"We are too! We are too!" cheeped the

shrews and voles. "We want supper."

"We'll be all right, won't we?" said
Mother Rabbit. "These cabbages look...."

She hopped up to one and sniffed it. Then
she opened her mouth to take a hungry bite.

"Stop!" yelled Fox suddenly. "There's
something wrong. Can't you smell it?"

"I don't care about smells," said Father
Rabbit. "If I don't eat soon, I'll die!"

"Fox is right," said Toad. "Haven't you
noticed? There are no animals in this field at
all — not even caterpillars, and they love
cabbages."

Owl hovered overhead.

"Beware! Beware!" she hooted. "Danger
is all around you. I've seen drums of poison
at the farm. Poison is in the air and on the
ground, and on the cabbages!"

"You mean the humans have poisoned
their own food?" said Vixen. "They must
be mad!"

"We must move on," said Fox.

The shrews and voles were very tired.

"It's not fair! We've got rights too," they
grumbled, but they scampered after Fox.

"Look! Trees!" said Squirrel suddenly.

The animals had come to an orchard.
Big red apples hung from the branches of
every tree.

 there's a town a long way off."

"Then I'll go and scavenge," said Fox.

"While we go hungry, I suppose," squeaked an angry shrew.

"Vixen, Owl and Whistler! Come with me," said Fox. "We'll bring food back for everyone. Put in your orders now!"

Owl led the way. It was very dark by now. Fox and Vixen slipped like shadows through

"Mmm! Juicy!" said Squirrel, bounding up the nearest trunk.

"I wouldn't eat them if I were you!" said Owl. "They might be poisoned too."

For a moment, they were all silent.

Then Owl spoke. "Well, Fox? What are we going to do?"

"What can you see, Kestrel?" asked Fox.

"Kee! Only fields!" called Kestrel. "But

the streets. Fox stopped outside a restaurant.

"I smell food!" he said. Fox and Vixen slipped down a side alley next to the restaurant, while Owl and Whistler rummaged through an upturned dustbin. Whistler found a fish and swallowed it.

"It tastes a bit odd, but it's a fish all right," he said cheerfully.

Back in the field, the smaller animals were trying to sleep.

"Was that thunder I heard?" said a vole, jumping nervously.

"No, only my tummy complaining," said Mole.

Adder looked at Mole and licked her lips.

"You're ssso delicsiousssly plump!" she hissed.

"You can't eat me!" squealed Mole. "Remember your promise!"

Suddenly Whistler landed, dropping a pile of food.

"Meat!" cackled Weasel, as she quickly grabbed a bite.

"For me!" hissed Adder, rearing up.

"Meat?" squeaked the voles and shrews. "We can't eat meat. Where's our supper? What about our rights?"

"Give me a chance," said Whistler wearily. "I'm going back for the vegetarian suppers."

Fox, Owl and Vixen left the restaurant and found a vegetable garden at the back of a house in the town.

Vixen dug up a lettuce. Owl picked it up in her claws and flew towards the field.

In the corner of the garden, Fox explored a dustbin. The lid was teetering on the edge of the bin when Fox accidentally knocked it to the ground. The lid clattered loudly onto the paving stones.

With a rush and a gnashing of teeth, two huge dogs bounded up, barking savagely. Fox and Vixen turned tail and streaked away through the garden gate, but the dogs were

dripping. A fence loomed up in front of Fox. He gathered himself for a great leap, and soared over it.

The dogs were no good at jumping. They stopped, and growled, and searched for a way through.

Fox looked around. In front of him were two metal rails that were rattling noisily. He looked up the line. A train was coming down the railway track.

right on their heels.

"Split up!" shouted Fox to Vixen, as he veered off to the right.

The dogs paused for a moment, and then they followed Fox, their powerful jaws

By now the dogs had found a way through the fence. One more moment and they'd be on him!

Fox had no choice. He darted across the railway line in front of the train! The dogs didn't dare follow him. He was safe now.

Dawn was breaking. Vixen made her way back to the anxious group of animals in the cabbage field.

"Where's Fox?" said Badger.

"I don't know," said Vixen sadly. She told him what had happened.

"He'll come back," said Badger, trying

to comfort her. "He always does. Now come along, everyone. We must get moving again." The animals hopped along through the endless rows of  cabbages. Suddenly, a butterfly flitted past Father Rabbit's nose. He sniffed at it, then sniffed longingly at a cabbage too.

"These cabbages smell all right to me," he said.

"Thisss butterfly isss sscrumptiousss," said Adder, snapping it up.

Father Rabbit opened his mouth to eat.

"We must leave here, quickly!" said Fox, running up.

"Oh Fox, you're safe!" said Vixen, and she nuzzled him happily.

"Listen everyone," said Fox urgently. "There's a tractor coming, and it's

spraying poison."

"Run away! Run away!" squealed Weasel, sprinting off in a panic.

"Come back, Weasel!" said Fox. "We must stick together. We can't all run fast enough to beat the tractor. Our only hope is to go back

to the parts of the field that have been poisoned already. The tractor won't go there again."

poisonous mist was rapidly covering the field. A butterfly got caught in the spray and fell dead at once.

The animals ran as fast as they could, but Father Rabbit tripped. The tractor roared up beside him. He couldn't run away in time.

"I've been sprayed! I've been sprayed!" he squealed, staggering after the others. He reached them and collapsed.

"Don't panic!" whimpered Mother Rabbit. "My poor husband...."

"He'll soon be fine, unless he dies of fright!" said Fox. "One spray of poison isn't strong enough to hurt a rabbit, but it will cause harm if you eat the crops."

Fox and Badger looked at each other over the heads of the other weary animals.

"What now, Fox?" said Badger quietly.

"We can't go all the way back through those awful fields," said Mother Rabbit.

"I'd never sssurvive," said Adder.

"Ha ha! Good thing if you didn't!" laughed Weasel.

Kestrel hovered overhead.

"Kee! I've seen White Deer Park!" she called. "It's just beyond the town!"

"Then we'll just have to go through the town," said Fox.

"But it's d-dangerous!" stammered Mole.

"There's no other way," said Fox. "Lead on, Toad. Our journey's nearly over."

"Go back through those silent fields?" wailed Father Rabbit.

"Kee! Quick! Be quick!" called Kestrel.

"Follow me! Now!" shouted Fox.

The tractor was very close now, and the

The Storm Shelter

The animals of Farthing Wood were on their way to White Deer Park, where humans couldn't destroy their homes. The route to safety now lay through the centre of town.

Weasel skipped along the pavement. "Weasels are wonderful..." she sang.

"Sssilence, Weasssel," Adder hissed.

There was a sudden rumble of thunder, and a bolt of lightning struck the pavement near Weasel. She danced about, howling.

"Ssserves you right," said Adder.

"A storm!" said Fox, looking up at the sky in dismay. "That's all we need."

A minute later, it was pouring with rain.

"I can't stand thunder," said Father Rabbit, trembling. "It ruins my nerves. And I'll catch my death of a cold."

Before long the gutters were full of swiftly flowing water.

"What will we do?" cheeped the mice and voles. "We can't cross the road!"

Owl had flown up to a nearby church.

"You've found a nice dry place to shelter from the storm," said Whistler, landing in the belfry beside her.

"Thanksss," Adder hissed as Whistler set her down on the green.

Everyone was feeling wet and miserable.

"Follow me to the church!" Fox said.

Owl glared at him. "I'm just getting a bird's eye view," she said.

Whistler peered out at the others. "Those little ones need help!" he said, and he took off again.

"Help! Help!" called the frightened mice and voles, as they struggled to swim across the flooded gutters.

One at a time, Whistler fished the animals out of the water with his beak and dropped them safely onto the muddy church green.

In the gutter, the stream of water was carrying Adder straight towards a drain, when suddenly Whistler swooped down and caught her in his mouth.

"There's sure to be a porch round the other side. We can shelter there."

But the old porch had fallen in.

"Now what will we do?" said Badger.

It was dark in the church, but at least it was dry. The animals nosed around to find comfortable places for themselves.

"We can rest now," said Fox. "Let's settle down and go to sleep."

A few minutes later, the only sounds were Badger's gentle snores.

Mole tugged at Badger's fur. "Let me get down, Badger, please," he said.

"Oh, all right, Moley," said Badger, "but don't start digging, will you?"

Mole slid to the ground, and ran off.

"Where's he going?" barked Fox. "Come back here, Mole!"

A few minutes later, Mole was back.

"Badger!" he squeaked. "I've found a way into the church! Come and see!"

Everyone followed Mole round to a hole, low down in the church wall.

"Well done, Moley," panted Badger, as he squeezed his big, furry body through the narrow gap.

The animals were so tired that they slept late the next morning. They didn't hear the workers clearing away the loose plaster from the gap in the wall. They didn't hear them fill it up with new stones, and cement over the cracks.

When they finally did wake up, it was too late.

"We're trapped!" Fox said. "We can't get out!"

"This is all your fault, Mole," said Father Rabbit meanly.

A tear rolled down Mole's fat cheek.

"It isn't anyone's fault," said Vixen.

"We had to get out of the rain and Mole found us some shelter."

"Thank you, Vixen," gulped Mole.

Toad scratched at his dry skin. "Wouldn't it be wonderful to be beside the pond in White Deer Park right now?" he said.

"Tell us about White Deer Park, Toad," said Vixen.

"Yes, tell us, Toad," clamoured the other animals excitedly.

Only Toad had ever been to White Deer Park, and the other animals were curious to find out more about their future home.

"Is it a big place?" asked Badger.

"The forest is enormous, mateys," said Toad dreamily. "And there are lots of animals there. The Great White Stag is the leader at White Deer Park. He is very kind, and his coat shines in the dark..."

"Listen!" said Fox. "What's that noise?"

The doors opened and the church filled with people dressed in their finest clothes.

"Run for it!" screamed Weasel.

"No!" said Fox. "Hide here, behind the organ, and wait until they've gone."

The animals waited. Suddenly there was a deafening, terrifying sound! The organs had started playing.

The mice had hidden in the organ pipes, but now a surge of air blew them right out of the top of the organ!

They landed with a crash on the keys of the organ. The surprised organist suddenly found a pair of mice running up and down under his fingers. As he tried to catch them, the music became a jangled blare of sound.

Weasel was dancing about behind the organ.

"Run! Run!" she squealed.

"Please, everyone. Keep still and wait," Badger growled. He clamped his great paw on top of Weasel to pin her down.

Mother Rabbit was quivering with fright. "Don't panic!" she whimpered.

She was too late. Father Rabbit darted out of the hiding place, and lolloped

down the aisle. Weasel wriggled free and scampered after him, followed by several of the smaller animals.

The people in the church panicked.

"Ugh! Help!" they shouted.

Some people tried to catch the animals, while others took fright.

"Hah! The humans are afraid!" chuckled Weasel. What fun she was having!

Then the doors swung open as the bride arrived at the church. The animals ran towards the open doors and freedom.

But Mole wasn't

fast enough. A large hand caught him by the tail. Badger heard his squeaks. He bared his teeth and growled at the man, then gently took Mole in his paw and placed him safely on his back.

"Oh thank you, Badger," said Mole, snuggling into his friend's furry shoulder.

Weasel was enjoying herself. She ran round the feet of a frightened lady, teasing her.

"Oo! Ow!" the lady shouted.

Owl was unlucky too. Her sharp claws got caught in the bride's veil. It floated off the bride's head and into the air.

Then suddenly, a shadow loomed overhead. Weasel looked up to see a man aiming to trap her beneath his top hat! She stopped laughing, and dashed out of the door.

The poor bride nearly fainted. Birds flapped overhead, and a badger, a mole, two foxes, a rabbit, a toad, a weasel and a whole collection of squirrels, mice, voles and shrews were milling about underfoot.

The bride threw up her hands in horror, accidentally throwing her flowers too.

"Very nice!" said Weasel, catching the bouquet. She began to play with it.

"Weasel, come on!" said Fox.

Weasel tossed the flowers into the air, and the bride's eager hands caught them. She tried to catch her veil, too, but it sank to the ground.

Whistler's long legs clipped a lady's hat as he flew out of the church, whisking it off her head.

Suddenly, something beneath the veil reared up, hissing. Adder wriggled free, and slithered out of the church.

"All'sss well that endsss well," she whispered, looking back through the church door.

The bride thought so too. She put on her veil, tidied her bouquet and marched up the aisle to her bridegroom. The organist, forgetting the mice, played an enthusiastic rendition of *Here Comes the Bride!*

The animals ran from the church, scattering in different directions.

The squirrels raced up a pole, chattering to each other. The rabbits panicked and fell into a ditch. Adder followed the smaller animals to a field of long grass.

Badger and Weasel raced away from the church, and ended up in the centre of town, where they found an open trap door. They dashed down the steep ramp and hid in the dark cellar.

Fox and Vixen were following Toad.

"White Deer Park is just across that field!" panted Toad. "Nearly there, mateys!"

"Slow down!" called Kestrel, from overhead. "Some of the animals are being left behind!"

"Oh no!" groaned Fox, looking back.

"They'll be okay," said Hare. "Let's go!"

"No," Fox said firmly. "We must find the others. After all we've been through on our journey, the animals of Farthing Wood will enter White Deer Park together."

White Deer Park was finally in reach.

From the crest of the hill Fox could see the beautiful waving treetops of the nature reserve. But the animals of Farthing Wood were scattered far and wide. They'd had a great fright, and had run off in different directions. Fox would have to gather all the animals, and lead them to the safety of White Deer Park together.

"We'll have to find the others," he said.

"Why?" asked Hare. "They'll find their way to the park on their own. Let's go now."

Mole looked worried. "We can't go without Badger," he said. "We won't leave Badger behind, will we, Fox?"

"Well, Fox?" called Owl from above. "You got us into this mess. How are you going to get us out of it?"

Badger and Weasel were hiding in town. They had slipped through a trap door and into a cool, dark storage cellar.

"This is fun!" said Weasel, dancing about on a stack of crates. "What an adventure!"

"Don't you care about the others?" growled Badger. "They might be in danger."

Weasel laughed. "Don't worry so much, Badger. I'm sure they're fine."

"I am worried, Weasel," said Badger seriously. "I think right now we should try to get some sleep. We'll need all our energy to search for Fox and Mole, and our other friends."

Weasel scampered down from the crates and slid across the floor. "Wheee! I'm having too much fun to sleep!"

On the edge of town, the squirrels were clinging to the top of a telephone pole, looking about for their friends.

"I can't see anyone," said one squirrel.

"Neither can I," said the other.

They didn't hear the squeaks of the voles, mice and shrews who were hiding in the long grass nearby.

There was a rustle in the grass, and Adder's forked tongue snapped out at the little animals.

"I thought I heard a sssqueak," she said.

The animals bolted with fear.

"What fun! Hide and ssseek!" hissed Adder, and she wriggled off after them.

Just outside the town, the rabbits had fallen into a deep ditch.

"I think I've broken my leg," wailed Father Rabbit.

"No, you haven't," replied Mother Rabbit. "You just like complaining."

"It's all right for you," grumbled Father Rabbit, "but I'm quite fragile." He hobbled about at the bottom of the ditch. "Oh dear, how are we going to get out of here?"

Back on the hilltop, Fox was thinking.

"This is a job for the birds," he said at last. "Owl, Kestrel and Whistler, you must go and find the other animals and bring them back here."

"Ridiculous idea!" hooted Owl. "They'll be in hiding. We'll never find them."

"But you're such a good hunter, Owl," said Fox. "Surely you'll be able to spot our friends."

"Very well," said Owl, looking pleased.

The three birds flew off into the sky.

Weasel was sleepy.

"Weasel, keep awake, please," said Badger crossly.

"I'm trying," replied Weasel with a yawn.

From outside came a thud. Then another thud, and another. A trolley piled high with crates rolled down the ramp into the storage cellar. Badger and Weasel dodged out of the way just in time!

Then Weasel did a quick U-turn, and leapt up the ramp and out to the street.

Badger followed, but he wasn't as quick as Weasel, and narrowly missed colliding with another trolley as it rolled down the ramp and into the cellar.

The stores manager gazed after the animals in astonishment as they raced past her.

By the time they rounded the corner, Weasel was exhausted.

"I'm so sleepy, Badger," she said, closing her eyes. "You'll have to carry me!"

Kestrel flew high in the air, scanning the ground with her powerful eyes.

"Kee! The squirrels!" she called, and dived down to the telephone pole.

The squirrels slid to the ground, chattering with relief.

"Follow me! Kee! Kee!" called Kestrel.

Fox saw the squirrels coming.

"Thank goodness you're safe!" he said. "Is there any sign of the others?"

"No," the squirrels replied, shaking their heads.

Mole began to cry.

"It's all right, matey," croaked Toad. "I know Badger's safe. I can feel it in my bones!"

Suddenly, the animals heard a grunting sound, and a weary Badger appeared. Weasel was fast asleep on his back.

"We've found you at last!" exclaimed Badger, looking round at his friends.

He stooped down, letting Weasel slide to the ground, where she continued to snore happily.

"Oh, Badger," said Mole, running to greet his friend. "I'm so happy to see you!"

Badger put out a great paw, and lifted the little animal into his arms.

The mice, voles and shrews had scurried away from Adder as quickly as they could. Now they came to a wide grassy slope.

"Is Adder still behind us?" asked a mouse.

Adder reared her head. "Yesss, I'm right here," she said. "Thisss game isss fun!"

The animals dashed into a sandy bunker.

in time, but Adder was too late. With a flick of her tail, she escaped down a golf hole.

"Bravo, Adder!" cried Kestrel.

Whistler found the rabbits in the ditch.

As Father Vole peered out, a golf ball whizzed past his nose! Kestrel's keen eyes spotted him, and she swooped down.

"Follow me!" she called.

As the animals scrambled onto the green, Kestrel spied a huge mowing machine approaching rapidly!

"Come on," she called. "Hurry!"

"Yesss, hurry!" hissed Adder, sliding up behind the frightened animals.

They sprinted away from the mower just

"Please get us out!" said Father Rabbit.

"Hmm, this could be tricky," said Whistler.

He bent down and Mother Rabbit hopped onto his back. Then she climbed up his long neck, and then with one more mighty hop, she was out of the ditch.

But Father Rabbit was too heavy. Whistler's legs sagged under the weight, and he couldn't stand up.

"I'll have to go for help," he said.

"You'll leave me

59

here. I know you will!" cried Father Rabbit. "Don't worry, I'll be back soon," Whistler replied calmly, as he flapped away.

He landed beside Fox.

"I've found the rabbits," he said. "Father Rabbit is stuck in a ditch."

"Well done, Whistler," said Fox. "I'll go and get them now."

"Do be careful, Fox," said Mole. "Rabbits can get into all kinds of trouble."

Fox found Father Rabbit sitting in a puddle at the bottom of the ditch.

"What took you so long?" grumbled

Father Rabbit. "I've got a broken leg, you know."

Fox ran down into the ditch. "Hop onto my back," he told Father Rabbit.

With a skip and a jump, they were out of the ditch.

"Er, thank you, Fox," said Father Rabbit.

Then he and Mother Rabbit hopped away.

"My pleasure," replied Fox, shaking his head in amusement.

By now Adder had found the rest of the animals. She leered greedily at a vole.

"I promisssed not to eat you during our journey," she hissed. "But the journey isss nearly over. I can't wait!"

Badger watched her slither away.

"Don't worry," he told the anxious voles. "Adder may want to behave like other

snakes, but I can see the journey has changed her. It's changed us all."

"I feel almost sad now the journey's over," said Father Vole.

"I'll be glad to arrive at White Deer Park," said Mother

Vole. "But even then we'll never be ordinary voles again. We're the animals of Farthing Wood, and we shall keep the spirit of our

journey for ever and ever."

"Well said, Mother Vole," said Fox. "And now, everyone, follow me. We are going to White Deer Park.

One by one, the animals entered the nature reserve. A huge stag was waiting to greet them.

"It's him, mateys!" gasped Toad. "The Great White Stag! We've made it at last!"

"Well done, my friends," the Stag said. "News of your great journey reached us long ago. Welcome to White Deer Park."

He turned, and the animals of Farthing Wood trotted after him into their new home.

Stories first published 1993 by Buzz Books
an imprint of Reed Children's Books
Michelin House, 81 Fulham Road, London SW3 6RB
and Auckland, Melbourne, Singapore and Toronto

This edition published 1994 by Dean
in association with Heinemann Young Books
Reprinted 1994

ISBN 0 603 55339 7

A CIP catalogue record for this book is available in the British Library

Produced by Mandarin Offset
Printed and bound in China